MW00994176

HOLE	1	2	3	4	5	6	7	8	9	OUT	
BLUE	315	327	416	551	155	393	322	480	143	3102	
WHITE	282	302	392	432	136	372	293	445	124	2778	
Dad	(4)	(4)	5	(5)	4	6	(3)	6	LOST BALL		
Anderson	7	5	7	(5)	6	7	7	9			
PAR	4	4	4	5	3	4	4	5	3	36	

This book belongs to

_____

_____

First U.S. edition 2022

ISBN: 9798365542785

Library of Congress Cataloging-in-publication
Data is available

Simply PUTT,
You're the best Dad by PAR.
The most wonderful Dad
In the HOLE wide world.
Today will be a TEE-rific day
FORE a round of golf.

- Author unknown

You play every weekend.
You and your friends have
fun.

If you keep losing golf balls,
soon there'll be none!

Are you picking the right club?

Is the wind in your face?

How is it possible that you're hitting the ball all over the place?

Maybe the ball should be bigger, then it wouldn't be so hard to find.

What if they attached a string to it? Then your score would...never mind.

I love playing with you, Dad.
Spending time with you is fun.

I can't think of a better pastime
for a father and his son.

The End

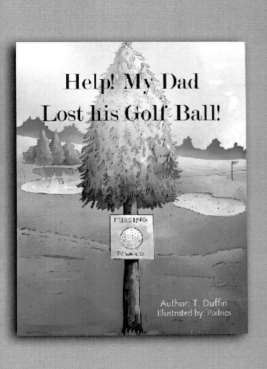

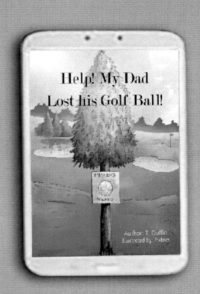

Join Anderson on his first adventure, *Help! My Dad Lost His Golf Ball!* Available at *tduffin.com.*

Thanks again for reading!

HOLE	1	2	3	4	5	6	7	8	9	OUT
BLUE	315	327	416	551	155	393	322	480	143	3102
WHITE	282	302	392	432	136	372	293	445	124	2778
Dad	④	④	5	⑤	4	6	③	6	LOST BALL	
Anderson	7	5	7	⑤	6	7	7	9		
PAR	4	4	4	5	3	4	4	5	3	36

Made in United States
North Haven, CT
15 September 2023

41607714R00015